PENGUIN BOOKS

Prayer for the Dead

James Oswald is the author of the Inspector McLean series of crime novels. The first six, *Natural Causes*, *The Book of Souls*, *The Hangman's Song*, *Dead Men's Bones*, *Prayer for the Dead* and *The Damage Done* are available as Penguin paperbacks and ebooks. He has also written an epic fantasy series, *The Ballad of Sir Benfro*, which is published by Penguin, as well as comic scripts and short stories.

In his spare time he runs a 350-acre livestock farm in north-east Fife, where he raises pedigree Highland cattle and New Zealand Romney sheep.

D0785571

By the same author

The Inspector McLean Series

Natural Causes
The Book of Souls
The Hangman's Song
Dead Men's Bones

The Ballad of Sir Benfro

Dreamwalker
The Rose Cord
The Golden Cage

Prayer for the Dead

A Detective Inspector McLean Mystery

JAMES OSWALD

PENGUIN BOOKS

PENGUIN BOOKS

UK | USA | Canada | Ireland | Australia
India | New Zealand | South Africa

Penguin Books is part of the Penguin Random House group of companies
whose addresses can be found at global.penguinrandomhouse.com.

First published by Michael Joseph, 2015
First published in Penguin Books, 2015
001

Copyright © James Oswald, 2015

The moral right of the author has been asserted

Set in 12.55/15.04 pt Garamond MT Std
Typeset by Jouve (UK), Milton Keynes
Printed in Great Britain by Clays Ltd, St Ives plc

A CIP catalogue record for this book is available from the British Library

ISBN: 978-1-405-93295-0

www.greenpenguin.co.uk

MIX
Paper from
responsible sources
FSC® C018179

Penguin Random House is committed to a
sustainable future for our business, our readers
and our planet. This book is made from Forest
Stewardship Council® certified paper.